Lean in the OR

Gerard Leone
Richard D. Rahn

Flow Publishing Inc.
Boulder, Colorado

Peter: Make every OR lean.

3/23/2011

ISBN-13:978-0-9713031-6-4
ISBN-10: 0-9713031-6-9

Table of Contents

Introduction

Is Lean, a philosophy and method originally developed in the world of manufacturing, applicable to an environment like an OR? After all, human beings are not products, and the complexity and variety of challenges found in the OR dwarf most manufactured products. These are some of the understandable questions and concerns that are raised when we talk about Lean in the OR. The concerns reveal, however, a lack of understanding about what Lean actually is. It may seem foreign or exotic, something that might work for a Toyota but certainly not for us.

There is no disagreement, however, that something needs to change. Healthcare costs are going up much faster than incomes or inflation, and something (one way or another) will need to give. It has been estimated that by the year 2020, personal income taxes would need to increase by 75% to cover the increase in government healthcare cost. Another source estimates that by 2020 the average household will be spending around $25,000 per year on health insurance alone. As a potential tool for healthcare improvement, let's take a look at some of the main characteristics of Lean, and see if we might have a fit in the OR.

Lean is based on the scientific method. Continual improvements are made by experimentation, trying things out, keeping what works and discarding what doesn't. The Lean improvement model is called PDCA, Plan-Do-Check-Act. This approach is 100% compatible with our goals in the OR, or for "evidence-based practice". There is certainly nothing exotic about this, other than the extraordinary focus that Lean organizations put on improvement.

Lean requires engagement. Lean is not about an outside expert coming into the OR and telling you how to do things the Lean way. It is team-based and requires the involvement and input of everyone in the department. Big changes may be needed, but often many small changes, suggested and implemented by department members, is what moves you forward.

Lean is primarily a philosophy. As opposed to being a collection of methods and tools, Lean is primarily a process improvement philosophy centered on the elimination of waste and improvement in patient flow. We may need to develop new tools and methods over time, but what is critical is a commitment to continuous improvement. There's a Japanese word for that: kaizen.

Lean is not a cost-cutting or a headcount reduction program. We do expect costs to drop, and the number of people we need may change as improvements are made. But people do not lose their jobs by making improvements, and costs will be lowered through a relentless focus on elimination of waste.

Another clear indication that Lean can be applied effectively in the OR is the fact that it is already being done. Although manufacturing has a 30 year head-start over hospitals in applying Lean, there are pioneers across the world that have been applying these methods for close to a decade. The commitment continues to grow within the hospital community and no one (as far as we know) have yet said "This won't work".

Following in this book are a series of eleven essays on various topics related to Lean in the OR. They are intended not to be a comprehensive analysis of each topic, but rather a way to get the juices flowing and the discussions happening. And while we don't think that Lean is the answer to all of the healthcare system challenges that we have, there is no doubt that it is making a big and positive contribution. Getting Lean is not an optional activity. It's a requirement!

Chapter 1: Eliminating Waste in the OR

If you are familiar with the concept of Lean Healthcare, you are familiar with the idea of waste. A Lean Hospital is an organization that is continually improving patient safety and satisfaction, treatment outcomes, and staff development through the elimination of waste, and improvement in patient flow.

Lean always goes hand-in-hand with the term waste. In this chapter we'll discuss the different forms of waste and some examples we would find in the OR and its associated services.

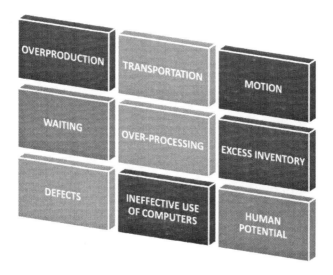

Overproduction. This form of waste takes place when we produce more than what is needed right now by the customer.

Examples of this waste in the Perioperative Services department are:

- Reassembling instrument sets in large batches while the autoclave sits idle. The symptom is "We do not have enough instrument sets."

- Spiking IV bags in Pre-Surgery for the whole day, while patients wait. The symptom is "Our on-time starts are very low."

You may think that over-producing is OK because you will need it eventually. Eventually is not now. Now is what matters, and now is when the patient is waiting. The time you missed you never get back, so do not over-produce.

Message to Charge Nurses and Clinical Managers: Do not make staff over-produce to keep them busy during a slow time. Have them do continuous improvement and you will get a great payback.

Transportation. We see this form of waste when the product or the patient (the value to be delivered) is moved without adding value.

Examples of this form of waste are:

- Blood specimens collected at the oncology unit go on a hospital tour before reaching the lab.

- IV and DVT pumps go from the patient room to Sterile Processing and back via utility rooms, for a few seconds of cleaning.

This waste is a bit more complex than saying "just stop doing that", as it was the case with over-production. This waste requires you to ask why in a more forceful way, and to come up with practical alternatives.

Motion. This form of waste refers to staff members moving without adding value. This becomes evident in the amount of walking staff members do during their day. They are normally looking or "hunting" for something. Why is it that we cannot provide clinicians with the tools and supplies they need to take care of patients?

Some examples of motion waste are:

- Searching for a patient lift, a positioning device, an IV pump or any piece of equipment. The level of frustration staff members feel when they cannot find what they need is enormous. Delay of care can also be dangerous for the patient.

- Searching for paperwork. If your hospital still requires hand-written paperwork for surgical patients, you may find yourself scrambling for that document while the patient is on the table.

This is one of the easiest forms of waste to solve. The application of 7S methods and the abolishment of the Par Level system for supplies management would get you 75% of the way.

Waiting. This is idle time created when supplies, information, people, or equipment is not ready.

If you find yourself waiting on any kind of service you need to start asking why, and be ready to take action once you get the answer. Just one rule: blaming somebody else is not allowed.

Take a stroll through the waiting rooms. How many patients do you see waiting? Go to pre-surgery. How many patients are ready, but their OR is not? Go to

PACU. How many patients are recovered, but there is no room for them to be moved to?

Over-processing. These are work steps that do not add value to the patient or customer.

This is the waste of overdoing. It is so easy to believe you are doing the right thing by overdoing. Think about the times you do this at home: "If three screws will do, five must be better".

In one Perioperative Services Department, staff was checking case carts four times, due to the unspoken distrust of the prior processes.

Excess Inventory. When you see more supplies, equipment or paperwork than what the customer needs right now, you have excess inventory. The OR is the champion of excess inventory in the hospital. The OR wants to have enough inventory in case the worst happens, and then double that in case the Martians attack.

Excess inventory gives staff a false sense of security. When you need something, you then have to wade through piles of stuff to get to what you need. Are you seeing the waste yet?

To that, add the increased risk of expired items due to the piles you have to go through. Pick a couple of well-stocked shelves and see if you find any expired supplies.

The main culprit is the incredible anachronistic Par Level system that many ORs use for supplies management. It is mind boggling that hospitals still use such an inefficient method to deliver supplies to clinicians. Start by abolishing Par.

The result of implementing Lean supplies management will be a substantial reduction in inventory dollars coupled with the elimination of shortages.

Defects. Defects represent work that contains errors, requires rework, has mistakes or lacks something necessary.

Nothing proclaims a broken process quite like defective work. The temptation is to start with the old search for accountability, and looking for someone to blame. Instead, try looking at the broken process and asking why, or use simple assessment tools like a fishbone diagram. Engage other staff members in finding solutions. The results will amaze you.

A typical OR example is that of an incomplete instrument set. Your choices are: "Accountability!" or, after you solve the immediate need ask: "Why was the set incomplete?"

- Could it be that it was sent to SPD from the OR incomplete?

- Could it be that we need to develop work instructions for each instrument set?

- Could it be that the instrument was sent to sharpening?

And the list goes on. What are you going to do once you get the answers?

Ineffective Use of Computers. This form of waste refers to time spent at the computer, not using the available software efficiently.

No one would question the fact that the use of computers is a must in the modern hospital. However, when their use detracts from patient care, we must stop and ask why.

Take another stroll and go to pre-surgery. Stand in the department and count the number of clinicians in patient rooms versus the number in front of a computer screen. What is the ratio? What should that ratio be?

Human Potential. The waste of human potential is not taking advantage of people's natural desire to be a part of something good.

This is the worst form of waste, because by engaging staff you will identify and reduce or eliminate all the other forms of waste. This is not about the touchy-feely stuff like "Our staff is our most valuable asset" or "we practice respect for our people".

Show respect for staff by engaging them in the solutions to the problems that afflict their processes. Check the results. You will be amazed.

Now is your turn. What forms of waste do you see in your OR? What is your plan to identify and eliminate it?

Chapter 2: Managing "A" Items in the OR

Imagine this: You walk into a local bank to open an account. As you're speaking to a bank representative, you notice that there are no tellers. Instead, customers seem to be walking into the unguarded vault and helping themselves, either depositing or taking the cash. The bank rep explains: "We can't really afford to hire people to just keep track of the cash, so we operate with the honor system. When you take some cash or drop some off, you are supposed to leave us a note. Once a month we'll do a count and reconcile the balances. Most people are pretty good at following the system, but we always have some variances to write up or down. But paying tellers to just keep track of the cash is a waste we just can't afford." By this time you're running for the door.

As ridiculous as this seems, this is exactly the way that many (most) hospital OR's handle their supplies and materials. Much of the material in the OR falls under the inventory classification of A items, items with a high dollar value. Examples of A items include implants, stents, and grafts. The dollar value of this material in the OR can easily total several million dollars or more, and represent 70% of your total inventory investment.

How do we keep track of all of these dollars, in the form of supplies? Very few OR departments actually maintain a perpetual inventory system, that keeps track of material like a bank keeps track of cash. In other words, at any given point in time the OR doesn't really know what is in stock without physically looking. Complete physical inventories are done periodically, sometimes as infrequently as every six months, and there are significant accounting write-ups or write-downs whenever this is done. Needless to say, this is a source of heartburn for the hospital financial department as well.

So why is this apparently common state of affairs, something that would be unacceptable in a bank or even a manufacturing company, allowed to continue in hospitals? Here are some of the reasons we hear:

1. Our focus is on the patient. We can't expect nurses and doctors to become "bean-counters". They're too busy.
2. Supplies and materials are often needed urgently. We can't slow down to fill out paperwork or transact what we need, because it's too time consuming.
3. We can't afford to hire any new FTEs to track materials, because that's just another overhead expense, and we need to control costs.
4. That's not the way things are done in a hospital.

Before we offer some suggestions for improvement, let's take a look at the hard costs related to lax inventory management. In that way we can make a more informed decision about what we can afford, or what level of attention to supplies might be needed. Here are some of the symptoms:

1. Shortages. If we don't know with precision what we have, then an inevitable result will be a higher level of shortages. The results can be serious for our patients, and also drive high expediting and overnight freight costs.
2. Inaccuracies in billing. Not everything gets billed out correctly if we don't have tight reins on inventory management.
3. Excessive supplies handling. The "par level" method used to assess inventory needs is horribly inefficient. It should be replaced with the system used by most world-class organizations, kanban. See the chapter in this book on Par and Kanban.
4. Inaccurate financial statements. The accounting rules tell us that if we don't really know what we have, we also don't really know what our costs are for any given financial reporting period.
5. Excess inventory. If inventory records are not accurate, we tend to compensate by overstocking. In a recent improvement project, we removed

over $500,000 in excess inventory from an OR, without breathing hard.

What should you do about managing A items? There are several possibilities, ranging from the very manual to the high tech. The simplest suggestion is to do what most high performing organizations do: have a quick-response stockroom in the OR, with individuals assigned to inventory control, inventory transactions, and patient service for materials. Set a goal of being able to put your hands on any item within 10 seconds, and set up the storage area to be able to accomplish this. Plan to staff the area for hours that match the schedule of OR need.

An intermediate-level solution would involve the use of bar-codes to speed up transactions and reduce errors. Nurses and techs can be trained to use the bar-code system, and reduce the workload on the materials staff. Barcoding is not a new technology, and virtually every inventory system supports it.

On the high-tech side, install RFID-based cabinets. An RFID cabinet is a locked storage container that is able to track what is inside via a Radio Frequency Identification tag attached to each high-dollar item. In order to unlock the cabinet an employee badge and a patient case number are needed. The RFID cabinet has the advantage of being able to capture billing information in addition to inventory information, and greatly reducing human error.

Regardless of the path you choose to follow, it is important to make a commitment to a high level of inventory control for A items in the OR. This effort will pay for itself many times over.

Chapter 3: The Par Level Myth Exposed

Story One: the keynote speaker at a recent regional meeting of APICS (American Production and Inventory Control Society) featured a high-level executive from a hospital material supply company, one of the largest in the country. After an informative but somewhat lackluster presentation, during the question period, a hand shot up. "How are Kanban methods being used in your hospital supply chain strategy?" was the question. After a short deer-in-the-headlights moment, the speaker responded: "What is Kanban?".

Story Two: a recent meeting in Las Vegas of hospital supply chain professionals featured a speaker on the topic of Kanban. The push-back from the crowd was tough, with person after person emotionally defending the Par Level system currently in use at their hospital. The speaker was able to answer each challenge well, but the debate came to a conclusion when one of the participants stood up and said "Hey guys. Let's be honest. Par Level doesn't work that well. Kanban is the future. Get over it."

There may be two questions in your mind at this point in the chapter: what is Par Level and what is Kanban? These two terms refer to methods used to manage supplies and materials, in a hospital or any place. We associate the Par Level system with hospitals because virtually no one else uses it, for reasons we shall see. Both methods share the idea that we should set up a target amount of material for any given item and location, never have more than that amount, and never run out. On these points the two methods are in agreement. Where they diverge is in the way that they propose to accomplish these goals.

The Par Level system proposes that we count the number of items remaining in a specific location, and simply replace the items that are needed to bring the quantity "up to par", i.e. back up to the target quantity. What could be easier, right? Of course that involves frequent counting, which is a wasteful and non-value-adding activity, and it requires frequent trips back to the stockroom, which is another wasteful and non-value-adding activity. Worst of all, the counting that is required is so onerous that most supply handlers don't do it, they simply "eye-ball" the materials and make an educated guess at the supplies to be refilled. Many supplies handlers are experienced and manage to keep on top of things most of the time, but as the saying goes, that's a hell of a way to run a railroad. The end result: certainly excessive effort and probably sub-par results as measured by shortages, organization of storage areas, and staff satisfaction.

As we said, the Kanban method has the same overall goals but approaches the replenishment process differently. Kanban is a Japanese word that means "signal", and creating a clear signal is at the heart of the Kanban method. Instead of counting everything all the time, Kanban proposes that we set up a signal system so that we can respond only to those items that need refilling. We do this by dividing the quantity to be stored into several sub-quantities. For example, we might take a par level of 100 pieces and divide it into two quantities of 50. No action is required until the first 50 are gone. We will then replace 50, but continue to use the remaining 50 during the refill process, so there is no delay of care for lack of supplies. The actual Kanban or signal could be an empty bin, a card that is removed and placed in a collection box, or a flag that is raised on the container itself.

This is not rocket science, but using the Kanban method can cut the number of items to be counted daily down to zero (none!) and the number of trips to the stockroom by at least 50%. This is the reason that Kanban is the method of choice for world-class organizations around the world. And it is also the reason why the Par Level system would never even be considered. We'll continue our discussion of Kanban in more detail in the following chapter.

Chapter 4: Kanban Systems in the OR

We have uncovered an opportunity that could mean millions of dollars in savings to individual hospitals, and billions of dollars to the healthcare system nationally in the US and abroad. It has to do with how most hospitals manage supplies, medications and other materials.

Many, maybe most, hospitals manage their inventory of supplies and medications using what is called a "par-level" method. It works like this: a stocking quantity is established for each item, the par level, based on average usage and a target number of days supply. We might, for example, set a goal of maintaining a two-day quantity of material for each supply item. As the material is actually used, we would bring the quantities "up to par" daily, by conducting a physical inventory and restocking the quantity that was consumed. The goal, sensibly, is to not run out of supplies while maintaining a tight control of storage space and inventory quantities. So far so good.

It is interesting to note that this par method of inventory control is not used in a world-class manufacturing environment, although a manufacturer certainly has the same needs and goals for inventory control as a hospital. The suggestion that we do a daily physical inventory for a large number of inventory items would be greeted with astonishment and ridicule. Many world-class manufacturing companies do not even conduct an annual inventory, by sustaining a high level of inventory accuracy through tight controls and cycle counting.

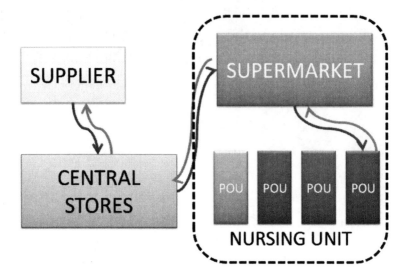

The method of choice in manufacturing for commonly used items is called Kanban. In a Kanban system, as with the par level method, we set a target quantity that we want to maintain. The principal difference is that instead of attempting to bring quantities "up to par" daily, in a Kanban system we set a fixed quantity that we will use to trigger the replenishment of inventory. In a "two-bin" kanban system, for example, we set up two quantities or bins of the same supply, and only refill a bin when it is empty. While the bin is being refilled, we have a second bin to cover usage during the replenishment cycle.

The Kanban method has seven main advantages over a Par-level system:

1. No daily counting is needed. We wait for a bin to be emptied and always replenish the same quantity. Not having to count can save hundreds or thousands of hours per year in most hospitals.

2. It reduces the number of resupply trips. Since we do not refill a Kanban bin daily, but instead wait for it to be empty, the number of replenishment trips can be reduced significantly. The number of replenishment cycles can be cut by 50% or more.

3. Replenishment quantities are fixed. The refilling process is greatly simplified by eliminating the need for counting required by the par system. If we know ahead of time what the refill quantity will be, the item can be stocked in that quantity.

4. It is easier to manage and improve. By tracking the time between replenishment, the stocking quantities can more easily be refined and adjusted over time. This continuous improvement is more

difficult to accomplish if all quantities are refilled daily, in varying quantities.

5. Kanban reduces inventory. Experience proves that, with the same target coverage of supplies, a Kanban system will run with up to 50% less inventory than a par system. This can be easily proven with a Kanban vs. Par simulation.

6. It is easier to maintain replenishment discipline. Since they do not have to count all inventory locations, or eye-ball the empty bins, supplies handlers find it easier to identify and refill the empty bins, thereby substantially reducing the opportunities for shortages.

7. Kanban promotes good inventory management practices, while the par level does not. In fact, counting everything is essentially impossible and very labor intensive, and most par-level users simply "eye-ball" the bins without counting. Organization and housekeeping, "5S" in lean terms, is much easier to maintain.

8. Kanban lends itself more easily to automation. Since the replenishment quantities are always the same, the computer can be a useful aid, whereas under the Par system the replenishment

quantities are continually changing (based on the daily counts).

For all of these reasons, Kanban is the method of choice for hospital material management, for much of the material that is procured and managed. The gains in productivity, reduced shortages and reduced inventory represent a multi-billion dollar opportunity for the industry.

Chapter 5: Standard Work in the OR

In 2011 we will be celebrating the 100th anniversary of the Fredrick Winslow Taylor's process improvement classic, *Principles of Scientific Management*. The book became a best-seller in the US, and also in Europe and Japan, and it was translated into over 10 languages within a year of its publication. Taylor proposed that we uncover and document the One Best Way to perform a work task, to train workers to do it that way, and then to continue to improve the method over time. This approach was applied to manufacturing work, and also to office and hospital processes. In the language of Lean, we call this Standard Work. As you can see, the concept of Standard Work is not new, and from our 21st century perspective the notion that standardization could be challenged seems quaint, but Taylor in fact did run into significant opposition in his time.

Let's recap the steps to follow in order to document work, from a Lean perspective. We first need to organize work into what we call "processes", groupings of similar work steps that take place in the same physical location and are done by the same type of resource. A grouping of processes to achieve a given outcome ("the value") is called a Value Stream, documented in a flow-chart format called a Value Stream Map. Each process on a Value Stream Map would need to be documented in detail, in what is called a Standard Work Definition or SWD. A Value Stream based on work done in the OR would follow a patient through from registration to discharge, and of course there are many different paths that the patient could take on that journey.

In creating a SWD we are interested primarily in three things: a description of the detailed work steps within the process, a reasonable estimate of the time required for each step, and a definition of the quality criteria for each step. This last requirement means this: if the work step can be done more than one way, but only one way is the right way, then it will be necessary to either redesign the process so that errors simply cannot occur ("error-proof") or double check the work before proceeding in the work sequence, and for that we must document the right way. In the case of critical or life-threatening steps, it will be necessary for two different people to confirm that the work step was done correctly. Just like taking off in an airplane, it is not sufficient for one person to do the work and check his/her own work if the step is critical. Two sets of eyes are necessary. Other data items that can be included on the SWD are machine vs. people time, changeover vs. work detail, a code for value-adding vs. non-value-adding steps, and supplies and equipment used.

In the Lean world, standardization has never been considered optional, but the complexity of modern Value Streams is making its use more and more essential. According to Atul Gawande, the author of *The Checklist Manifesto*, the era of the Master Builder in healthcare is drawing to a close. In construction the Master Builder would design the building, and also oversee all aspects of the construction and manage to project. Working in this way, a successful outcome, i.e. the building doesn't fall down, is dependent largely on the individual skill of the Master Builder, and not on a well-designed and defined process. The Master Builder method of construction was overwhelmed by modern complexity by the middle of the last century and is no longer used. The Master Building mentality still exists in healthcare, but it is also in the process of being overwhelmed. In its place is a multi-disciplinary approach with a foundation of Standard Work.

Value Stream										
Process			STANDARD WORK DEFINITION						LEAN HOSPITAL	
SWD Name										
Date Created										
Revision										

Order	Description of Work Performed	Supplies	NVA Y/N	Divisible Y/N	Machine Time	Person Time	Transport	TQM Check	Self-check Description

One way to gain perspective on the importance of Standard Work is through the lens of the Process Maturity Scale. By classifying a work process along a scale of five levels of maturity, we can determine the appropriate effort required to improve and sustain improvements in a process. The key point is this: changes made in a process that is not mature are at risk of not sustaining. Let's examine each of the levels, starting with Level 1.

At Level 1, the lowest level, the process has a name and an owner. Naming the process simply means that a grouping of work steps has been given a process name, like "case cart picking" or "OR suite changeover". Many individual work steps are required to change over the operating room, but it is still only one process. The owner of a process is the individual within the organization responsible for documenting the work, training staff to do the work that way, processing improvement ideas, maintaining metrics and auditing process performance. Getting to Level 1 is a positive step forward, but it is not nearly enough to ensure sustainability of process improvements.

At Level 2 we have documented the work in detail, using the Standard Work Definition form shown above, and the method discussed earlier in this chapter. Accomplishing this level can be time consuming, especially if there are a lot of work steps, and a lot a variants of the process. The work times that we document should be "reasonable and generous"; we're not trying to capture the time for the fastest person, but instead we are trying a document a reasonable average time. The work is best documented by observing or video-taping a number of difference experienced people. Note that in the OR we are primarily talking about operational work, and not procedure work, but opportunities abound there as well.

At Level 3 we have trained and certified the people doing the work in the documented process. It does little good to document the One Best Way to do something, if the workforce is not actually doing it. The training and certification process would normally be done under the guidance of a Master Trainer, and certification would be earned by performing the correct work steps while being observed by the Master Trainer. It will be additionally important to continue to audit Standard Work in a process, and this is normally the daily responsibility of managers and supervisors. An employee training status board is maintained in the OR, and kept current.

At Level 4 we are introducing "kaizen" or continuous improvement. Once a process has been stabilized through Level 3, there is no assumption that we have arrived at perfection; any process can be improved. We will want to have one or more key performance metrics that we track, and solicit ideas and input from the people working in the process. Every process should have a "Target Condition", a goal or next improvement that the team is working towards, under the leadership of the Process Owner. Once that goal has been reached, the next Target Condition will be defined. One of our Lean slogans is "What Gets Measured Gets Done". Every process on the OR Value Stream Map should always have a target condition that is being pursued.

At Level 5, we are able to sustain a trend of continuous improvement in the process. To declare that the process is at Level 5 it will be necessary to provide evidence of at least a 12-month track record of improvements in the key performance metrics that we established at Level 4. Achieving and sustaining Level 5 is especially important since if a process is not being actively improved, chances are excellent that it is actually degrading.

The value of a Process Maturity Scale and assessment is that if we are not at least at Level 3, it will be difficult or impossible to sustain process improvements, and kaizen efforts will be a waste of time. A strong foundation of Standard Work can therefore be considered a prerequisite for improvement. Concentrating improvement efforts on the OR will yield great benefits, since that is where a large percentage of the hospital revenue, material usage and process complexity reside.

Chapter 6: Quick Changeover in the OR

The time was the late 1950's. Struggling to survive after near-bankruptcy in the early part of the decade, the Toyota Motor Company had dedicated itself to rebuilding, and to the ideal of "kaizen" or continuous improvement in all of its processes. One of the challenges they faced was excessively long changeover times on their large presses, the machines that stamp out body parts. They had discovered that one of their competitors was able to change over the identical machine in three hours from one part to another, as compared to Toyota's current best time of six hours. They had assigned the task of reducing the time to at least equal the competition to a young engineer named Shigeo Shingo, and after several months of team effort he was ready to report the results.

"We had achieved our goal," Shingo reported in his autobiography, "and we were proud to be able to report success. However, after the initial congratulations from the plant manager, he gave us our next assignment. What I want you to do, he said, is to now reduce the time from three hours to three minutes. We all thought he was literally crazy." After the initial shock wore off, and because he couldn't say no, the wheels began to turn in Shingo's mind, and the light bulb went on when he realized that the goal was not to eliminate three hours of labor time, but to reduce the time that the expensive piece of equipment was unavailable for use. This insight was the beginning of what we now call SMED, Single Minute Exchange of Dies, or quick changeover in less than 10 minutes.

So what, after this rather long-winded introduction, does this have to do with the OR? What does an OR have in common with a large Japanese stamping machine? Let's ask, and answer, a series of questions.

1. Are OR changeovers within the single-minute range? No.

2. Is the operating room an expensive asset that we'd like to utilize as much as possible? Yes.

3. Does an OR require an extensive and complex changeover time between procedures? Yes.

4. Can this changeover time be reduced, without compromising safety and patient care? Almost certainly Yes.

From this initial assessment, it is clear that quick changeovers in the OR are not only beneficial, they are also very feasible. The chief benefit for a hospital in reducing changeover time is to increase the potential utilization of this resource, to have more intra-operative time to perform proper checklist-driven time-outs or meticulous instrument counts, schedule more procedures with the same number of rooms, and avoid highly expensive construction of new ORs.

So how might SMED be applied to an OR environment? A *spaghetti diagram* as shown below shows the amount of walking required in a room changeover, for example. Reducing the amount of walking by restructuring the work flow could reduce the room changeover time significantly.

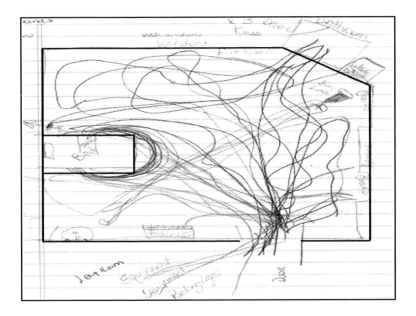

Let's introduce the topic of SMED by stating clearly that quick changeover does not include any reduction in standards or quality. Quick Changeover does not mean rushing, hence increasing the number of errors. If anything our expectation is to improve the quality of work done, not reduce it.

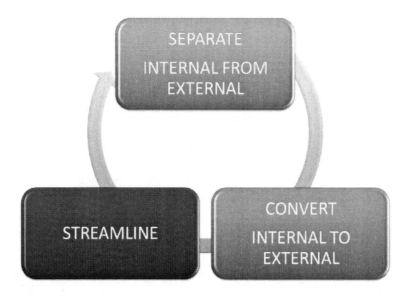

Step one in the SMED process is called *Separate Internal from External*. This means that anything that can be done while the prior procedure is still going should be done ahead of time. By "external" we mean a work step or action that can be done outside or external to the procedure. For example, if you start to search for that C-Arm or Harmonic Scalpel when the prior procedure is already completed, you are consuming "internal" time and lengthening the changeover time. If, on the other hand, the equipment is located and staged while the prior procedure is still going on, you have reduced the changeover time. This step may seem to be common sense, but as we know, common sense things are not always done.

The second step in the SMED process requires more creativity: *Convert Internal to External*. Step one was the easy stuff, but in step two you actually look for ways to change the existing process so that you can do what are currently internal step as external steps. At Toyota the breakthrough was to do the changeover work on a removable fixture, outside of the press. When it came time to change from one part to another, the old die could be quickly removed and the new die installed and locked into place within a few minutes. In an OR you would look for similar opportunities to move preparation work ahead of time, by mixing disinfectants outside the room and staging them or by maintaining duplicate sets of the most common, least expensive, equipment, for example. There may be some investment required, but that cost would have to be justified by significant additional utilization gained in the OR.

The third and final step in the SMED process for ORs is called *Streamlining*. This simply means doing what you do more efficiently. Standard Lean tools like 7S (5S +2), Kanban, and Waste Elimination are valuable here. In a recent OR quick changeover project that we worked on, 20 minutes of time that had been spent "looking for things" was eliminated through a robust 7S and Kanban effort. Streamlining can be applied to both internal and external steps, with a priority on reducing internal steps first.

The recommended starting point for a SMED initiative is to train your team in the process. You can then move to understanding and documenting in detail the current state, where you are today, warts and all. Videotaping is a valuable aid in doing a detailed analysis, since both the work steps and times can be capture simultaneously. Write down each discrete work step, along with the work minutes and the resource needed. As a team-based effort you can then apply the SMED process starting with separating internal from external steps.

How much can you expect to reduce OR changeover time? If, like the Toyota stamping plant, you set ambitious goals for yourself, and don't give up, then great improvements can be expected. Given the cost of today's OR resources, however, even modest time gains are well worth the effort as they are likely to yield great benefits for the patient and for the hospital.

Chapter 7: Instrument Set Flow in the OR

The Lean OR, or in more inclusive terms the Lean Perioperative Services Department, can turn instrument sets quickly and with perfect quality. This may sound like a fairy tale to many of you, so let us first define what "quickly" means. To turn instrument sets quickly means that the lead-time for a given instrument set must be as close as possible to the time it actually takes to decontaminate, wash, reassemble, wrap, and sterilize the instruments. We refer to this as the ability to "flow" instrument sets.

Let's assume a very simple sequence of processes from the time an OR surgical case is finished to the moment the instrument set is ready to be picked for the next case:

Spray -> Transport -> Decontaminate -> Wash -> Cool -> Reassemble -> Wrap -> Sterilize -> Store

Each of the steps above is what in Lean terms we call a "process". The sequence of all processes to deliver a unit of value to a customer is called a Value Stream. There are three major stages in developing a Lean value stream capable of flowing instrument sets:

- Calculate resources and design the physical layout

- Bring live and manage the value stream
- Sustain the changes

To fully design a value stream capable of flowing instrument sets in the fastest possible manner we must:

Define the Product. The product is the individual instrument set. Since there are many variations, we recommend classifying them into groupings by specialty and size. To keep things manageable, use Large-Medium-Small. The amount of work content is directly related to the size of the set.

Gather Volumes. Not all instrument sets are used equally. If your hospital performs many Ortho surgeries, your knee sets and ortho minor surgical sets will get a lot of usage, while your cysto sets may rarely see the light of the OR suite. You will have to figure out how to get this usage data. If you have an instrument tracking system, that should be your first stop. If you trust your EMR's intra-operative notes, look at them. There is always the possibility to have to gather the data manually. We have done this and it is not that difficult. The goal is to have a figure of daily usage per instrument set.

Define the Work. This is achieved by drawing a Process Flow Diagram (PFD) per instrument set. A PFD show the sequence of processes an instrument set follows. Patterns will start to emerge from this. The machine-washed sets that are wrapped follow a different processing path than the hand-washed peel-packed instruments. We are likely to end with a dozen different PFDs to cover all instrument sets.

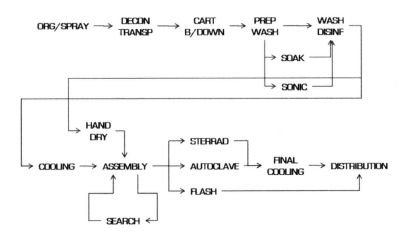

• **Identify Families**. We must now analyze the PFDs and find groups of sets that share a common processing path. There may be two or three PFDs that are very close. These families of sets will give us the first indication of what physical processes should be co-located to minimize travel distances. This is normally achieved by creating a "Set-to-Process matrix". Picture a matrix with all instrument sets (or groups) as rows and all processes as columns. Every time a set goes through a process, place an "X" at the intersection.

Gather Standard Times Per Process. This is probably your most laborious step. Go back to the prior step. Everywhere you see an "X" in the matrix, it must be replaced with the time it take to do the work in that process for that set. There may be some repetition and you might be able to use estimates, but it is a very good idea to reach for the stop-watch.

Calculate Resources. The resource calculations are remarkably simple, yet they require a great deal of experience to interpret. The calculation is as follows:

$$Resources = Standard\ Time\ /\ Takt$$
$$Takt = Work\ time\ /\ Volume$$

Develop a Conceptual Layout. This layout is your first pass to locate resources (people, machines, and inventory) in a block layout without any regard to the existing constraints. This is a highly recommended exercise, as it will give you a glance into the possibilities of an "ideal" layout.

Develop the Actual Layout. Working on the blueprint of the available area and the picture of the conceptual layout, place all the resources in physical locations that most closely resemble the conceptual layout.

You now have the blueprint of your new sterile processing department. You now must develop a plan to move all the resources, train staff in the new way of flowing sets, and begin the acquisition process of any new equipment you may need. A note on new equipment: resist your urge to buy stuff. Do all you can to redesign your department with the existing resources. A good redesign will not require any more capital equipment than what you have.

The next stage of your project is to bring live the department and manage the new instrument set flow. The live process must be done with the assistance of the entire process improvement team and the performance of the department must be closely monitored. You should plan to hit your stride within a few days. Keep a close eye on the expected performance as compared to actual performance and act swiftly if necessary. If the calculations show that the department should be able to flow a set in 160 minutes and you are not hitting this average response time within 3-to-5 days, you must take action. This may be a case of faulty assumptions, or an unexpected glut of hard cases that use large sets. Whatever the case, you cannot afford to wait and see.

To ensure the sustainability of results, you have to set up four key elements of a Lean Value Stream:

Standard Work for Leaders. The idea behind this sustainability feature is that Standard Work applies to all in a Lean Value Stream. The closer we are to the value (the instrument set) the more standardized our work is. As an example, for a SPD the team established an "end-of-day checklist" for the department manager. This list had to be completed and signed off at the end of each day.

Daily Accountability Process. This refers to setting up daily checkpoints, in the form of brief meetings, for all the team members in the department to ensure that all aspects of the value stream are being managed.

Visual Controls. The Lean Value Stream moves fast, and it is very important to have the ability to check the status of the department by quickly scanning a series of visual controls. Examples are completion charts, statistical process control charts, and the instrument cooling rack (overflowing vs. empty).

Discipline. This is what makes Lean work. Lead by example and allow no exceptions to the rules and the established processes. If there is a need for an exception, look for ways to standardize the change.

This should give you a good starting point to get started with the Lean transformation in your Sterile Processing Department.

Chapter 8: Is the Invasive Center the Future?

In a recent conversation with the chief architect at one of the leading healthcare architectural firms, he indicated that many prospective clients are demanding hospital designs compliant with Lean principles. He was not sure his clients fully understood what that meant. In all fairness, neither did the architect himself.

What hospital executives know, or foresee, is that the current sybaritic approach to healthcare spending will come to an end within their professional lives. This issue is of critical proportions at hospitals which now consume more than 30% of total healthcare spending in the US. This is one of many reasons why hospitals need to do more with fewer resources. That was the original definition of "Lean".

Less what, you may ask? Less floor space, shorter length of stay, faster lab response times, quicker imaging readings, and the list goes on and on. In case you worry that what is coming is "less people", relax. There is so much waste to eliminate and so many opportunities to turn that waste into better patient care that cutting staff is at the bottom of the list.

Leonardo Group Americas has had first-hand experience with the actual design and implementation of the "Invasive Center". This is a single department within a hospital where all invasive procedures take place. The exact make-up of the department would depend on the services offered by your institution. The Invasive Center we helped design includes the OR Suites, Interventional Radiology Suites, Cardiac Catheterization Labs, Endoscopy rooms, Lithotripsy room, and Minor Procedure rooms. All these services will share common Registration, Pre-Surgical Care Unit, PACU I, and PACU II functions.

The productivity promises to be higher, and the level of care and teamwork is bound to improve substantially, in a smaller footprint, as compared to all the services separately.

Some issues to consider in planning for an Invasive Center:

- Figure out patient flow before the architectural design. Do not expect the architects to have any knowledge of Lean patient flow. It is not their specialty, regardless of how good they are.

- Plan for supplies management before you call the architects. Supplies at a hospital are the epitome of an afterthought. Materials managers at most hospitals are 30 years behind the latest thinking in materials management, and is not a wonder that this is the top complaint we hear in every new Lean implementation we undertake at hospitals.

- Make plans for the use of perpetual inventory disciplines. This is one of those puzzling issues in healthcare: uncontrolled inventory. This is unthinkable in any other line of business that uses supplies or materials. No, we do not know why it is the way it is.

- Develop a strategy for case cart management. When we say "case cart" we think "surgery". You may choose to use case carts for all cases in the Invasive Center. Plan for the path coming into the procedure rooms and going back to SPD. Consider using the method of "In-process Kanbans" (IPKs). The case cart IPK would cause you to pull the next case cart when a procedure was completed, not when we have some spare time to pick. This would limit the number of carts picked and staged, as well as the number of returns whenever a procedure is canceled.

- Plan for staff flexibility. This is a must for the Invasive Center. The idea that a clinician will sit in the Cath Lab waiting for a patient that is being prepared for the procedure must be abolished. The concept we apply is the one we call "flexing". Every time you find yourself without the ability to move a patient to the next care process you must ask "why?" and react accordingly. If the room is ready and the patient has not arrived, the most likely cause is that is taking longer to prepare the patient than anticipated. Move upstream from the Cath Lab to Pre-Surgery and help prep your patient. Conversely, if the procedure is done, you may need to help with recovering your patient if there is blockage downstream. There will be some limitations as to what clinicians can do to "flex" from process to process and hospital administration need to look into possible incentives to facilitate it.

These are just some pointers to get you thinking. The main and overarching issue is to do your homework before you call the architects. After you started construction, the issues will be very similar to implementing Lean in your current building. You would like to avoid having to deal with a building that is not conducive to productivity, quality, and flexibility.

Chapter 9: Staff Engagement in the OR

One of the most important differences between an organization that is achieving great benefits from their process improvement efforts and an organization with so-so results is the level of employee engagement. In a truly Lean organization, everyone understands that it is not enough to simply do your job well, and that everyone is expected to participate in the improvement work in every process. This chapter documents this type of effort in a hospital OR department with an informal program they called "Fix-it Fridays".

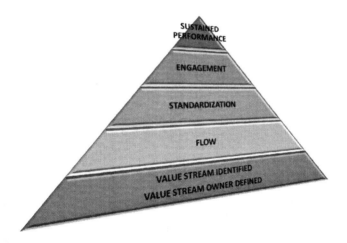

A core concept in Lean Thinking is that of a Value Stream, and the technique of Value Stream Mapping is typically one of the first steps in launching a Lean effort.

In order to measure the maturity of a value stream, we've developed the Value Stream Maturity Scale. This pyramid suggests that a value stream matures as it progresses though different levels.

The levels, leading to sustained performance, are:

Level 1: The Value Stream is identified and ownership is assigned. Think of a typical value stream in a hospital, Medication Management. It starts at the time when the MD places the order and ends when the meds are administered to the patient. All the processes in between those two points make up the value stream.

Level 2: Flow. The value (the medication) progresses from process to process in an uninterrupted fashion. Achieving flow is not a one-time event, but a progression through a series of improvement iterations.

Level 3: Standardization. The processes within the value stream are standardized to the level of work instructions. Not all processes can be standardized in a clinical setting, but those that can be standardized must be.

Level 4: Engagement. This is the Holy Grail of Lean. Staff members participate in the identification of waste and engage in projects to seek the elimination of wasteful activities.

Just think of the power of every staff member in the OR focusing on eliminating waste. Here are several examples:

During a project to redesign a Sterile Processing Department, the entire team was coming at 6:00 a.m. every day, for a week, to bring live the area after the design was finished. On Wednesday, we all arrived to realize that the OR started late on Wednesdays, so we had nothing to do for three hours. Within 5 minutes, a team member said "Hey guys, why wait for instruments? Couldn't we do some of the 7S stuff we learned about in class?" BINGO! We split into three teams of 2 or 3 team members to work on different areas. By the time the first set arrived from the OR the team had completed three separate 7S projects, with the following results:

- We found two surgical stools that were scheduled to be re-purchased.

- We identified and re-located approximately $5,000 in "orphan" instruments that were stashed in a drawer to be dealt with at a later date. Nobody knew how long they had been there.

- We reorganized the unload area for the cart wash, saving ~1 minute per case cart.

Those are just the highlights. The real value was the sense of accomplishment that followed those mini-projects. This team became unstoppable after that.

Another person who took this idea of engagement to heart was Beth. Beth was the Manager for the Cardiovascular Services Department for a large city hospital. Fridays were usually very slow days for her department. Being an outstanding cook, she organized social lunches on Fridays for all her staff. After working with us for a few months, she realized that Fridays could be a great opportunity for something more than social time. She still provided lunch, but Beth re-branded the event "Fix-it Fridays".

Fix-it Fridays meant to get together as a team, enjoy lunch, and then take one topic from the list of continuous improvement suggestions to implement right then and there. The results were nothing short of remarkable. Beth was so successful that she was asked to tackle a very sore spot at the hospital: their overly-long Door-to-Balloon time. Under Beth's leadership, they reduced Door-to-Balloon time by more than 60%.

There is no magic in the cases above. There is engagement. There is respect for staff and their ideas.

There is leadership in finding the time to do continuous improvement.

It is not that difficult. Go ahead, give it a try.

Chapter 10: Prioritizing Instrument Sets

We know of no OR that has enough instrument sets to take care of all the cases within a surgeon's block time. This apparent shortage is aggravated by the way in which instrument sets are batch processed from the OR to the Sterile Processing Department (SPD) and back. In this chapter, we will discuss one case where simple low-tech tools were used to identify the priorities for SPD processing of instrument sets. This improvement was made as a Lean Kaizen event, where a team of knowledgeable people dedicated a week of time to address the problem.

After the team documented, analyzed, and re-designed the entire SPD, the shortages of instrument sets plummeted. Block time scheduling for surgeons, however, places a high burden on the instrument set inventory because the block demand is a very high spike of usage rather than a smooth curve. Assuming that block times would not be changed, we had to look for ways to prioritize the instrument sets returning to SPD after a case was finished and ways to flag and prioritize the various demands placed on SPD services.

The new design for the SPD started on the "dirty" side with a queuing area coming out of the return elevator, organized in first-in, first-out fashion. This organized the case carts and avoided "cherry-picking", i.e. selecting the easier carts first. There are several different conditions for processing instrument sets:

- Normal Processing. No special expediting is necessary.
- Rush: The instrument is needed sooner than normal. Move up in the queue.
- STAT: The instrument is needed on an expedited basis, but it is to be wrapped and sterilized in SPD.
- STAT FLASH: The instrument is needed on an urgent basis and it must be flash-sterilized in the OR for immediate use.

Knowing under which condition a set returns to SPD is very important. This is usually communicated via frantic calls and even trips from the OR to SPD. Put your Lean thinking hat on and tally the number of minutes spent on the phone chasing instrument sets. See the waste?

Following is the process that the Kaizen team developed, using the Lean tools of Visual Management. Based on the classifications mentioned above, every time a case is completed the following steps take place. These were documented for the Perioperative Services Team using Standard Work definitions:

- Return all instruments to their respective pans.
- Apply enzymatic foam to all appropriate instruments.
- Gather all refuse and place it on top of the case cart.
- Move case cart to the staging area in front of the "dirty" elevator.
- Apply a color-coded clip to the instrument set, according to how this set is to be treated in the SPD. This is normally done by the Service Line Coordinator.
- Return the case cart to the SPD.
- Process instrument set according to the clip color code.

The SPD Tech interprets the clips as follows:

- No clip: Normal processing. Process the cart via first-in, first-out (FIFO) priority all the way through the SPD.
- Yellow clip: The case cart moves to the front of the first FIFO lane in the decontamination area. After that it is processed normally.
- Red clip: STAT processing. The case cart jumps to the front of the first FIFO lane in the decontamination area. After that it receives

expedited processing. The instrument set is sterilized in the SPD.

- White Clip: The case cart moves to the front of the first FIFO lane. After that it receives expedited processing. The instrument set is flashed-sterilized in the OR.

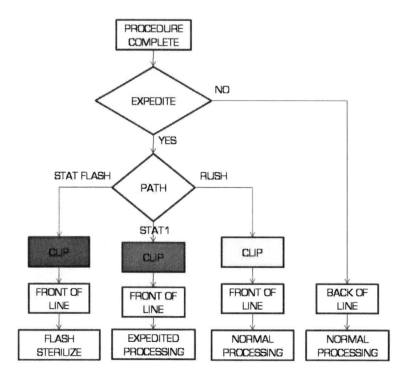

Simple Visual Management tools like the use of color-coded clips can eliminate the waste of calls and chasing, by indicating what needs to be done visually. There are many other applications of visual management that are possible throughout any hospital. .

Chapter 11: Use of Checklists in the OR

In his recent book *The Checklist Manifesto*, Dr. Atul Gawande describes in great detail the creation of the World Health Organization's Safe Surgery Checklist. Checklists for healthcare were first discussed by Gawande in an article in the December 2007 issue of The New Yorker titled (what else?) *The Checklist*. The central point of this article is how the use of a 5-point checklist helped in dramatically reducing infection rates associated with the insertion of central lines. There you have it, one shining example of the power of the humble checklist. Why then are healthcare professionals so slow are at adopting standardization practices in their daily work?

Standard Work is not your enemy! There is a misconception among clinicians that by standardizing some of the repetitive tasks they do every day, they will lose the autonomy that characterizes their professions. Nothing could be farther from the truth. By making repetitive work predictable, you save your energies for the unpredictable. For example, by making sure that there is a clear and repeatable procedure to assemble case carts and deliver all the required supplies to the OR prior to the surgery, you can dedicate all your energies to the patient, and not to hunting for supplies or wondering if everything you need is there. Do not be afraid of standard work, just trust your judgment as to what processes should and should not be standardized in your clinical work.

Checklists are a tool to aid with standardized work. They aim at ensuring repeatability of certain critical elements of work. Wash hands with soap, *check*. Clean procedure area with chlorhexadine, *check*. We are all humans and we are bound to forget something, no matter how small, when we are immersed in the non-stop world of the OR. Observations of work in ICUs show a rate of error for around 1%, or an average of two mistakes per patient!

What checklists should we adapt? The WHO Safe Surgery Checklist is one of them, check. How about a checklist for the Pre-Surgery department to ensure that every patient receives all the necessary care and talks to every required clinician before being wheeled to the OR? What about a checklist to ensure that every patient has all the necessary documentation before the day of Surgery? How about a checklist for the OR Suite changeover? The opportunities are vast, once you put your mind to it.

Clinicians and OR Nurses are not opposed to checklists or other tools for standardizing work. They do, however, have a problem with being told what to do. Here is a recommendation: be pro-active. By being against something you are on the losing side of the issue. The next time something does not go as planned, you might be slapped with another checklist developed by some external expert that may have no knowledge of your processes and culture. Cross the road to the sunny side and embrace the Culture of Continuous Improvement that Lean brings to the OR.

Next time you see a process that has some weaknesses and potential failure points, organize an OR team for a Kaizen project. Outsiders and consultants are welcome, but this is your project, not somebody else's. Plan for a maximum of three days to complete the project and deliver a functional checklist. Evaluate the process and figure out the critical work elements that may lead to failure. Test the checklist with staff. Do a quick pilot run, make tweaks, implement it, observe the new process, gather performance data, and prepare a quick presentation to tell your success story. Here are a few pointers that may help you develop an effective checklist:

Decide on the type of checklist. A *Do-Confirm* checklist assumes that team members work independently from memory until they stop to go over the checklist to confirm that the right steps were completed. With a *Read-Do* checklist one team member carries out the tasks while another one reads each task and checks them off as they are completed.

Make it short. It is a checklist, not a training manual. The checklist is not there to tell you how to do the job. Think index card, rather than legal size paper.

- Keep wording precise and simple while avoiding unnecessary clutter and coloring.
- Turn the brain on. The checklist must help you turn your brain on when you are using it. A checklist is not a replacement for a brain.
- Test the checklist. There is a very good chance that your first draft will need revision. Do not be discouraged, but correct it and try again.

Healthcare around the world is at a crossroads, evolving from a craftsman-style delivery of care to the creation of an integrated healthcare delivery system. This change is necessary, both to improve patient outcomes and to reduce costs that are growing at an unsustainable rate. The use of checklists will be a powerful tool in this transformation. Being left behind is entirely up to you.

Leonardo Group Americas (LGA)

The mission of *Leonardo Group Americas* is to assist its clients to achieve success with the implementation of advanced Lean methods in the factory, hospital and the office. This is accomplished through our talented people and their profound knowledge and experience, a suite of world-class training seminars, books and materials, and through the prudent application of lean software tools.

LGA has been involved with the deployment of Lean in hospitals since 2002, and is a founding member of the Lean Hospital Group. They have conducted Lean improvement projects in virtually every hospital process and Value Stream.

Find out more about Leonardo Group Americas at www.leonardogroupamericas.com and www.leanhospitalgroup.com, or send us an email at contact@leonardogroupamericas.com.